VOCAL SCORE

OF

THE MIKADO;

OR,

THE TOWN OF TITIPU.

BY

W. S. GILBERT

AND

ARTHUR SULLIVAN.

Vocal Score (complete) .. Price, net 20/-

CHAPPELL & CO., Ltd., 50, NEW BOND ST., LONDON, W. 1
AND SYDNEY.
CHAPPELL & CO Inc., NEW YORK

THE MIKADO;

OR
THE TOWN OF TITIPU

DRAMATIS PERSONAE.

THE MIKADO OF JAPAN.

NANKI-POO (*his Son, disguised as a wandering minstrel, and in love with* YUM-YUM).

KO-KO (*Lord High Executioner of Titipu*).

POOH-BAH (*Lord High Everything Else*).

PISH-TUSH (*a Noble Lord*).

YUM-YUM

PITTI-SING   *Three Sisters—Wards of* KO-KO.

PEEP-BO

KATISHA (*an elderly Lady, in love with* NANKI-POO).

CHORUS OF SCHOOL-GIRLS, NOBLES, GUARDS, AND COOLIES.

ACT I.—Courtyard of Ko-Ko's Official Residence.

ACT II.— Ko-Ko's Garden.

THE MIKADO.

CONTENTS.

Vocal Score.

THE MIKADO.

Or, The Town of Titipu.

OVERTURE.

SECONDO.

THE MIKADO.
Or, The Town of Titipu.

OVERTURE.

PRIMO.

SECONDO.

SECONDO.

SECONDO.

SECONDO.

SECONDO.

PRIMO.

SECONDO.

Nº 1.

CHORUS OF MEN.

PIANO.

Allegro vivace. (♩ = 126.)

CHORUS of TENORS & BASSES
in *Unison.*

If you

want to know who we are,_____ We are gen-tle-men of Ja-

-pan:_____ On__ ma-ny a vase and jar—

On__ ma-ny a screen and fan,_____

We figure in live-ly paint,— Our

at-ti-tude's queer and quaint— You're wrong if you think it ain't._____

Oh,

Unison.

If you think we are work'd by strings,

Like a Jap-an-ese ma-rio-nette,

You

don't understand these things:

It is sim-ply Court e-ti-

-quette.

Per-

gen_tle_men of Ja _ pan:_____ On vase and

gen_tle_men of Ja _ pan:_____ On vase and

jar, On screen and fan, On ma_ny, ma_ny, ma_ny, ma_ny,

jar, On screen and fan, On ma_ny, ma_ny, ma_ny, ma_ny,

ma_ny, ma_ny, ma_ny, ma_ny a jar, Oh!_____ oh!_____

ma_ny ma_ny ma_ny ma_ny a jar, Oh!_____ oh!_____

Segue Nº 2.

Nº 2.

SONG and CHORUS—(Nanki-Poo).

Allegro marziale.

But if pa_tri_o_tic sen_ti_ment is want_ed, I've pa_tri_o_tic bal_lads cut and dried; For wher_e'er our country's ban_ner may be plant_ed, All o_ther lo_cal ban_ners are de_fied! Our war_ri_ors, in ser_ried ranks as_sem_bled, Ne_ver quail—or they conceal it if they do— And I shouldn't be surpris'd if na_tions

trem_bled Be_fore the mighty troops, the troops of Ti - ti - pu!

MEN. *f*
We shouldn't be surpris'd if

Na_tions trembled, trembled with a_larm Be_fore the mighty troops, the troops of Ti - ti -

Allegro pesante, non troppo vivo. (♩ = 160.)

NANKI.

- pu!
And if you call for a song of the sea, We'll

heave the cap_stan round, With a yeo heave ho, for the wind is_free, Her anchor's a-trip and her

fid_dler swings us round, With a yeo heave ho, And a rum be_low, Hur_rah for the homeward

fid_dler swings us round, With a yeo heave ho, And a rum be_low, Hur_rah for the homeward

bound!__ With a yeo heave ho,____ And a rum be _ low,____ Yeo-

bound!__ With a yeo heave ho,____ And a rum be _ low,____ Yeo-

-ho, heave ho, Yeo - ho, heave ho, heave ho, heave ho, yeo - ho!

-ho, heave ho,____ Yeo - ho,____ heave ho, heave ho, heave ho, yeo - ho!

SONG—(Pish-Tush)—and CHORUS.

be be _ head _ ed.

And I ex _ pect you'll all a _ gree That he was right to so de _ cree. And

I am right, And you are right, And all is right as right can be!

MEN. And you are right, And

And all is right as right can

we are right, And all is right, is right as right can be! And all is right as right can

36

18056

youth who wink'd a rov_ing eye, Or breath'd a non-con _ nu_bial sigh, Was there-up_on con_

_demned to die— He u_sual_ly ob_ject_ed, ob_ject_ed, ob_ject_ _ _ _

_ed, He u_sual_ly ob_ject_ed.

And you'll al_low, as I ex_pect, That

he was right to so object. And I am right, And you are right, And ev_'ry_thing is

quite cor_rect!

MEN. *f*

And you are right, And we are right, And ev_'ry_thing is quite, is quite cor_

E

And ev_'ry_thing is quite cor_rect, All____ is quite____ cor_

rect, And ev'ry_thing is quite cor_rect, All____ is quite____ cor_

_ rect!____

_ rect!____

ff

And so we straight let out on bail A convict from the coun_ty jail, Whose

p

head was next On some pre-text Con-demn-ed to be mown off, And made *him* Headsman

for we said "Who's next to be de - ca - pi-ted Can-not cut off an - o-ther's head Un - til he's cut his

own off, his own off, his own_____ off, un-til he's cut his own off."

And we are right, I

think you'll say, To ar-gue in this kind of way. And I am right, And you are right, And all is right-too-

- loo - ral - lay!

MEN. *f*

And you are right, And we are right, And all is right— Too - loo - ral, loo - ral -

And I am right And you are right, And all is

-lay! And you are right, And we are right, And all is

a tempo

right!

a tempo

right!

SONG — Pooh-Bah (with Nanki-Poo and Pish-Tush.)

Allegro moderato. (Tempo di Minuetto.) (♩=106.)

PIANO.

POOH-BAH.

Young man, despair, Like — wise go to, Yum - Yum the fair You must not woo. It will not do: I'm sor _ ry for you, You ve _ ry im _ per _ fect a _ blu _ tioner! This

ve ‿ ry day From school Yum-Yum

Will

wend her way, And home ‿ ward come, With beat of drum, And a

rum ‿ tum ‿ tum, To wed the Lord High Ex ‿ e ‿ cu ‿ tion ‿ er!

And the brass will crash, And the

trum ‿ pets bray, And they'll cut a dash On their wed ‿ ding day, She'll

2. It's a hope _ less case, As you may see, And in your place A _ way I'd flee; But don't blame me— I'm sor _ ry to be Of your plea _ sure a di _ min _ u _ tion _ er.

They'll vow their pact Extreme _ ly soon,

In point of fact This af_ter_noon Her
ho_ney_moon With that buf_foon At seven,com_men_ces, so___
you shun her! And the
brass will crash, And the trum_pets bray, And they'll cut a dash On their wed_ding
day, She'll toddle a_way, as all a_ver, With the Lord High Ex_e_

_cu _ tion-er!

NANKI & PISH.

And the brass will crash, And the trum _pets bray, And they'll

cut a dash On their wed _ ding day. She'll tod_dle a _ way, as

She'll tod_dle a _ way, as

all a_ ver, With the Lord High Ex _ e _ cu _ tion-er.

all a_ ver, With the Lord High Ex _ e _ cu _ tion-er.

RECIT.— (Nanki-Poo and Pooh-Bah.)

RECIT. NANKI.

VOICE.

And have I journey'd for a month, or near_ly, To learn that Yum-Yum,

PIANO.

whom I love so dear_ly, This day to Ko_ko is to be u_ni_ted!

RECIT. POOH-BAH.

The fact ap_pears to be as you've re_ci_ted:

a tempo moderato

RECIT.

But here he comes, e_

a tempo

_quipped as suits his sta_tion, He'll give you a_ny fur_ther in_for_ma_tion.

Attacca Nº 5.

CHORUS.-(with Solo—Ko-ko.)

TENORS.

Be_hold the Lord High Ex - e - cu _ tion_er! A

BASSES. *f*

Be_hold the Lord High Ex - e - cu _ tion_er! A

jail

By a set of cu_rious chan'_ces;

Ta_ken from the coun'ty jail,

Lib_er_a_ted then on

Ta_ken from the coun_ty jail,

Lib_er_a_ted then on

Sure_ly, ne_ver had a male So ad_ven_tur_ous a

bail, Sure_ly, ne_ver had a male So ad_ven_tur_ous a

bail, Sure_ly, ne_ver had a male So ad_ven_tur_ous a

tale.

tale. De _ fer,_____ de _ fer,_____ To the Lord High Ex_e_

tale. De _ fer,_____ de _ fer,_____ To the Lord High Ex_e_

54

18056

SONG—(Ko-Ko, with Chorus of Men.)

persons who in shaking hands, shake hands with you like *that—* And all third persons who on spoiling
doesn't think she dan_ces but would ra_ther like to try;" And that sin_gu_lar an_o_ma_ly, the

A

CHORUS OF MEN.

tête - a-têtes in_sist— They'd none of 'em be miss'd— they'd none of 'em be miss'd! He's
la_dy no_vel_ist— I don't think she'd be miss'd— I'm *sure* she'd not be miss'd! He's

He's
He's

got 'em on the list— he's got 'em on the list; And they'll none of 'em be miss'd— they'll
got her on the list— he's got her on the list; And I don't think she'll be miss'd— I'm

got 'em on the list— he's got 'em on the list; And they'll none of 'em be miss'd— They'll
got her on the list— he's got her on the list; And I don't think she'll be miss'd— I'm

KO-KO.

none of 'em be miss'd! 2. There's the *Ni_si Pri_us* nuisance, who just
sure she'll not be miss'd! 3. And that

none of 'em be miss'd!
sure she'll not be miss'd!

now is ra_ther rife, The Ju _ di_cial hu_mor_ist— I've got *him* on the list! All

fun_ny fel_lows,com_ic men, and clowns of pri_vate life— They'd none of 'em be miss'd— they'd

none of 'em be miss'd! And a _ po_lo_ge_tic statesmen of a compromis_ing kind, Such as—

what-d'ye call him-Thing'em-bob,and like_wise_Ne_ver Mind,   And 'St— 'st— 'st— and What's-his-name,and

colla voce

al _ so You-know-who— The task of fill_ing up the blanks I'd ra_ther leave to *you.* But it

real_ly does_n't mat_ter whom you put up _ on the list, For they'd none of 'em be miss'd— they'd

CHORUS OF MEN.

none of 'em be miss'd! You may put 'em on the list— you may put 'em on the list; And they'll

You may put 'em on the list— you may put 'em on the list; And they'll

none of 'em be miss'd—they'll none of 'em be miss'd!

none of 'em be miss'd—they'll none of 'em be miss'd!

CHORUS OF GIRLS.

Comes a train of little ladies

60

18056

From scho-las-tic tram-mels free, _____ And we won - der how we
won - der, We won - der— how—we won - der!— What on
earth the world can be! What on earth__ the
world__ can be!

Attacca Nº 7.

№ 7. TRIO — (Yum-Yum, Peep-Bo, and Pitti-Sing) — with Chorus of Girls.

B

Three lit_tle maids from school.

Three lit_tle maids from school.

Three lit_tle maids from school.

Three lit_tle maids who, all un_wa_ry,

Three lit_tle maids who, all un_wa_ry,

Three lit_tle maids who, all un_wa_ry,

Come from a la_dies' se_mi_na_ry, Freed from its ge_nius tu_te_la_ry—

Come from a la_dies' se_mi_na_ry, Freed from its ge_nius tu_te_la_ry—

Come from a la_dies' se_mi_na_ry, Freed from its ge_nius tu_te_la_ry—

Three lit_tle maids from school, Three lit_tle maids___ from school.

Three lit_tle maids from school, Three lit_tle maids___ from school.

Three lit_tle maids from school, Three lit_tle maids___ from school.

One lit_tle maid is a bride, Yum-Yum—

Two lit_tle maids in at_ten_dance come—

Three lit_tle maids from school!

Three lit_tle maids from school!

Three lit_tle maids is the to_tal sum. Three lit_tle maids from school!

D

From three lit_tle maids take one a_way—

Two lit_tle maids re_main, and they—

Won't have to wait ve_ry long, they say—

QUARTET.— (Yum-Yum, Peep-Bo, Pitti-Sing & Pooh-Bah,)
with Chorus of Girls.

youth, of course, must have its fling, So par‿don us, So par‿don us,

PITTI-SING.
And don't, in girl‿hood's

hap‿py spring, Be hard on us, Be hard on us, If we're in‿clined to dance and

YUM-YUM.
But youth, of course, must

PEEP-BO.
But youth, of course, must

sing, Tra la la la la la, But youth, of course, must

CHORUS OF GIRLS.
Tra la la la la la, Tra la la la la la, Tra la la la la la, Tra la la la la

la la la la la la la!

la la la la la la la!

la la la la la la la!

la la la la la la la!

POOH-BAH.

think you ought to re_col_lect You can_not show too much res_pect To_wards the highly ti_tled

E

few; But no_bo_dy does, and why should you? That youth at us should have its fling, Is

hard on us, Is hard on us; To our pre_ro_ga_tive we cling— So par_don us, So

F

YUM-YUM.

But

PEEP-BO.

But

PITTI-SING.

But

par_don us, If we de_cline to dance and sing—Tra la la la la la, Tra la la la la

F

youth, of course, must have its fling, So par_don us, And

youth, of course, must have its fling, So par_don us, And

youth, of course, must have its fling, So par_don us, And

la, Tra la la la la la, Tra la la la la la, Tra la la la la la, Tra la la la la

don't, in girl_ _hood's hap_py spring, Be hard on us.

don't, in girl_ _hood's hap_py spring, Be hard on us.

don't, in girl_ _hood's hap_py spring, Be hard on us.

la, Tra la la la la la, Tra la la la la la, Tra la la la la la la la!

CHORUS. f

But

DUET—(Yum-Yum and Nanki-Poo.)

YUM-YUM.

This, oh, this— oh, this— oh, this— this,___

ne - ver do! This, oh, this— oh, this— oh, this— this___

He'll ne—ver do! He'll ne—ver do!

— is what I'll ne—ver do! I'll ne—ver do! Oh,

This is what he'll ne—ver, ne—ver do!

this, this is what I'll ne—ver, ne—ver do!

TRIO—(Ko-Ko, Pooh-Bah and Pish-Tush.)

Allegro non troppo vivace. (♩=84.) POOH-BAH.

VOICE.

I am so proud, If, I al-lowed My

PIANO.

fa-mi-ly pride To be my guide, I'd vo-lun-teer To quit this sphere, In-stead of you, In a

minute or two. But fam'ly pride Must be— de-nied, And set a-side, And mor-ti-fied, And

KO-KO.

mor— ti-fied. My brain it teems With endless schemes, Both good and new For Titi-

-pu, For Ti - ti - pu; But if I flit, The be - ne - fit That I'd dif - fuse The town would lose! Now

ev_'ry man To aid his clan Should plot and plan As best he can.

PISH-TUSH.

I heard one day, A gentleman say That criminals who Are cut in two Can hard_ly feel The

fa _ tal steel, And so are slain, are slain Without much pain. If this is true, It's jol_ly for you; Your courage

POOH-BAH.

screw To bid us a_dieu.

I

PISH-TUSH.

I heard one day, A gentleman say That criminals who Are

KO-KO.

My brain it teems＿＿＿ With endless schemes, Both good and new For Ti_ti_

am so proud, If I al＿lowed My fa＿mi＿ly pride To

cut in two Can hardly feel The fa＿tal steel, And so are slain, are slain Without much pain. If this is

_pu, For Ti_ti_pu; But if I flit, The be_ne_fit That I'd dif＿fuse The town would lose! Now

be my guide, I'd vol＿un＿teer To quit this sphere In_

true, It's jol_ly for you; Your courage screw To bid us a_dieu.

ev'ry man To aid his clan Should plot and plan As best he can.

And

_stead of you, In a min＿ute or two.

so, Although I'm rea_dy to go, . Yet re_col_lect 'Twere dis_res_pect Did

POOH-BAH.

I neg_lect To thus ef_fect This aim_ di_rect, So I ob_ject— And

so, Although I wish_ to go, And great_ly pine To bright_ly shine, And

PISH-TUSH.

And-go And show Both friend and foe How

take the line Of a he_ro fine, With grief condign I must decline.

much you dare. I'm quite aware It's your af_fair. Yet I declare I'd take your share, But I don't much

life - long lock, A _ waiting the sen _ sa _ tion of a short, sharp shock, From a

cheap and chip _ py chopper on a big black block! To sit in sol _ emn si _ lence in a

dull, dark dock, In a pes _ ti _ len _ tial pri _ son, with a life - long lock, A _

-waiting the sen_sa_tion of a short, sharp shock, From a cheap and chippy chopper on a

big black block! A dull, dark dock, A life - long lock, A

short, sharp shock, A big black block! To sit in sol_emn si_lence In a

FINALE—ACT I.

Don't he_si_tate   Your choice to name,   A dread_ful

Don't he_si_tate   Your choice to name,   A dread_ful

fate You'll suf _ fer all the same,   A dread_ful   fate You'll

fate You'll suf _ fer all the same,   A dread_ful   fate You'll

POOH-BAH.

To

suf _ fer all the   same.

suf _ fer all the   same.

94

18056

yields his life if I'll Yum-Yum sur_ren_der; Now I a_dore that

girl with passion tender, And could not yield her with a rea_dy will, Or her al_lot,

If I did not A_dore my_self with pas_ _ sion ten_d'rer still! With

pas_sion ten_d'rer still!

CHORUS.

Ah, yes! He loves him_self with passion ten_d'rer still!

Ah, yes! He loves him_self with passion ten_d'rer still!

KO-KO.

Take her— she's yours!

Allegro con brio. (= 132.)

YUM-YUM.

And bright _ ly shines the dawn _ ing

NANKI-POO.

The threat_en'd cloud has pass'd a _ way,

day;   There's yet   a   month of af _ ter_noon!

PEEP-BO.

Then

NANKI-POO.

What tho' the night may come too   soon,

Then

POOH-BAH & PISH-TUSH.

Then

shout! Laugh_ing_ song, mer_ry_ dance, with_laugh'_ing_ song and_ mer_ry_

_reer Laugh_ing song, mer_ry dance,with laugh_ing song and mer_ry

_reer Laugh_ing song, mer_ry dance,with laugh_ing song and mer_ry

_reer Laugh_ing song, mer_ry dance,with laugh_ing song and mer_ry

dance.

dance.

dance.

POOH-BAH. SOLO.

dance. As in a month you've got to die, If Ko_Ko tells us

true, 'Twere emp_ty com_pli_ment to cry"Long life to Nan_ki - Poo!" But as one month you

Allegro agitato.

Oh fool, that flee-est My hal _ low'd joys! Oh blind, that see _ est No e _ _ qui _ poise!

Oh rash, that judg _ est From half, the whole!

Oh base, that grudgest Love's light _ est _ dole! Thy

heart un _ bind, Oh fool, oh blind! Give me my place, Oh rash, oh

lots of good fish in the sea! There are lots of good fish in the sea! There's lots of good

lots of good fish in the sea! There are lots of good fish in the sea! There's lots of good

fish, good fish in the sea! There's lots of good fish, good fish in the sea, in the sea, in the

fish, good fish in the sea! There's lots of good fish, good fish in the sea, in the sea, in the

sea, in the sea, in the sea!

sea, in the sea, in the sea!

Andante. KATISHA.

The hour of glad_ness Is dead and gone; In si_lent

sad_ness I live a_lone! The hope I cher_ish'd All life_less

cresc.

lies, And all has per_ish'd, all has per_ish'd Save love,___which never

sempre f *Allegro agitato* RECIT.

dies, Which nev_er, nev_er dies! Oh, faith_less one, this

in_sult you shall rue! In vain for mer_cy on your knees you'll

-pour With an-gry growl! Do ye your worst, my ven-geance call Shall rise tri-

TUTTI.

-umph-ant o-ver all! We'll hear no more, Ill-o-men'd owl, To joy we

più f

soar, Des-pite your scowl; The e-choes of our fes-ti-val Shall rise tri-

KATISHA.

-umph-ant o-ver all! Pre-pare for woe, Ye

meno f

haugh-ty—lords, At once I—go Mi-

wrongs with__ ven - geance shall__ be__ crown'd!

_ff_

We do not heed their

_ff_

We do not heed their

cresc.

_ff_

dis - mal__ sound, For joy reigns ev - 'ry - where__ a - round! We

dis - mal sound, For joy reigns ev - 'ry - where a - round! We

do not heed their dis - mal__ sound, For joy reigns ev - 'ry - where__ a -

do not heed their dis - mal sound, For joy reigns ev - 'ry - where a -

KATISHA.

My wrongs with ven - geance shall be crown'd, My

_round! We do not heed their dis_mal sound, For

_round! We do not heed their dis_mal sound, For

wrongs with ven - geance shall be crown'd!

joy reigns ev - 'ry - where a - round!

joy reigns ev - 'ry - where a - round!

con forza
ff

18056

END OF ACT I

Act II.

SOLO.—(Pitti-Sing, & Chorus of Girls.)

126

18056

When you're sum-moned, start, Like a fright-ened roe—

Flut-ter, lit-tle heart, Col-our, come and go!

Mo-des-ty at mar-riage-tide___ Well be-comes a

pret-ty bride!_____ Mo-des-ty at mar-riage-tide Well be-

-comes a___ pret-ty bride!

Braid the ra - ven hair_ Weave the sup _ _ ple tress— Deck the mai _den

Braid the ra - ven hair— Weave the sup _ _ ple tress— Deck the mai _den

fair_ In her love _ _ li _ ness— Paint the pret _ ty face— Dye the

fair_ In her love _ _ li _ ness— Paint the pret _ ty face— Dye the

co _ ral lip— Em _ phasize the grace Of her la _ dy - ship!

co _ ral lip— Em _ phasize the grace Of her la _ dy - ship!

Nº 2.   SONG— (Yum-Yum.)

She bor_rows light That, thro' the night, Mankind may all ac _ claim her!

And, truth to tell, She lights up well, So I, for one, don't blame her. Ah,

pray make no mis _ take, ___ We are not shy; We're ve _ ry wide a _ wake, ___

p
cresc.

___ The moon and I! Ah, pray make no mis _ take, We are not shy; We're

dim.

ve_ry wide a_wake, The moon and I!

rall.
a tempo
mf
p

№ 3. MADRIGAL–(Yum-Yum, Pitti-Sing, Nanki-Poo and Pish-Tush.)

fleet _ ing? Fic _ kle mo _ ment, pri _ thee stay! Fic _ kle _ mo _ ment, pri _ thee
weep _ ing, Till the sad sun-down is near, Till the _ sad sun-down is

fleet _ ing? Fic _ kle mo _ ment, pri _ thee stay! Fic _ kle mo _ ment, pri _ thee
weep _ ing, Till the sad sun-down is near, Till the sad sun-down is

fleet _ ing? Fic _ kle mo _ ment, pri _ thee stay! Fic _ kle mo _ ment, pri _ thee
weep _ ing, Till the sad sun-down is near, Till the sad sun-down is

fleet _ ing? Fic _ kle mo _ ment, pri _ thee stay! Fic _ kle mo _ ment, pri _ thee
weep _ ing, Till the sad sun-down is near, Till the sad sun-down is

stay!
near.

stay!,
near,   Plea _ sures
                                                                        I to -

stay!
near.

stay!
near.

                                        What though mor _ tal _ joys be hol _ low?
                                        All must sip the _ cup of sor _ row—

dong! Ding dong! Yet un _ til the sha _ dows fall O _ ver
dong! Ding dong! What, though sol _ emn shadows fall, Soon _ er,

dong! Ding dong! Yet un _ til the sha _ dows fall O _ ver
dong! Ding dong! What, though sol _ emn shadows fall, Soon _ er,

Ding dong! Ding dong! Yet un _ til the sha _ dows fall O _ ver
Ding dong! Ding dong! What, though sol _ emn shadows fall, Soon _ er,

dong! Ding dong! Yet un _ til the sha _ dows fall O _ ver
dong! Ding dong! What, though sol _ emn shadows fall, Soon _ er,

one and o _ ver _ all, Sing a mer _ ry, ma _ dri _ gal, Sing a _ mer _ ry madri _
la _ ter, o _ ver _ all? Sing a mer _ ry, ma _ dri _ gal, Sing a _ mer _ ry ma _ dri _

one and o _ ver _ all, Sing a _ mer _ ry madri _
la _ ter, o _ ver _ all? Sing a _ mer _ ry madri _

one and o _ ver _ all, Sing a mer _ ry ma _ dri _
la _ ter, o _ ver _ all? Sing a mer _ ry ma _ dri _

one and o _ ver _ all, Sing a mer _ ry ma _ dri _
la _ ter, o _ ver _ all? Sing a mer _ ry ma _ dri _

TRIO.—(Yum-Yum, Nanki-Poo, & Ko-ko.)

In a month, or less, I must die with _ out a wed _ ding! Let the bit _ ter

tears I'm shed _ ding Wit _ ness my dis _ tress, Here's a pret _ ty mess!

Here's a pret _ ty mess! KO-KO. Here's a state of things!

To her life she clings! Ma _ tri _ mo _ ni _ al de _ vo _ tion Does _ n't seem to

suit her no _ tion— Bu _ ri _ al it brings! Here's a state of things!

For if what he says is true, I can_not, can_not mar_ry you! Here's a

For if what he says is true, I can_not, can_not mar_ry you! Here's a

For if what I say is true, he can_not, can_not mar_ry you! Here's a

stringendo

pret _ ty, pret _ ty state of things!

pret _ ty, pret _ ty state of things!

pret _ ty, pret _ ty state of things!

stringendo

Spoken.

Here's a pret_ty how-de-do!

Here's a pret_ty how-de-do!

Here's a pret_ty how-de-do!

Nº 5.

Entrance of Mikado and Katisha.

Mi_ya sa_ma, mi_ya sa_ma, On n'm_ma no ma_yé ni Hir_ra_Hir_ra su_ru no wa

Mi_ya sa_ma, mi_ya sa_ma, On n'm_ma no ma_yé ni Hir_ra_Hir_ra su_ru no wa

Nan_ gia na___ To_ko ton _ ya _ ré ton _ ya _ ré na!

Nan_ gia na___ To_ko ton _ ya _ ré ton _ ya _ ré na!

MIKADO.

daughter-in-law e _ lect! My _ na_ture is love and light— My free_dom from

KATISHA.

all _ de _ fect— Is in _ sig_ni_fi_cant quite, Compar'd with his daughter-in-law e _

_ lect! Bow! Bow! To his daughter-in-law e _ lect!

CHORUS.

Bow! Bow! To his daugh_ter-in-law e _ lect.

Bow! Bow! To his daugh_ter-in-law e _ lect.

dim.

dim.

Attacca Nº 6.

SONG—(Mikado.) and CHORUS.

ob _ ject all sub _ lime____ I shall a_chieve in time— To

let the pun_ish_ment fit the crime, The pun_ish_ment fit the crime; And

make each pris _ 'ner pent Un _ wil_ling_ly re _ pre _ sent A

source of in_no_cent mer _ ri_ment, Of in_no_cent mer _ ri _ ment!

pro _ sy dull so _ ci _ e _ ty sinners, Who chat_ter and bleat and bore,_____ Are
ad _ ver_tis _ ing quack whowearies With tales of count _ less cures,_____ His

sent to hear sermons From mys_ti_cal Germans Who preach from ten till four. The
teeth, I've en_act_ed, Shall all be ex_tract_ed By ter_ri_fied a _ ma_teurs. The

a _ ma_teur te_nor, whose vo _ cal vil _ la_nies All de _ sire_ to shirk, Shall,
mu_sic-hall sing_er at _ tends a se_ries Of mass_es and fugues and "ops" By

du_ring off-hours, Ex _ hi_bit his pow_ers To MadameTus_saud's wax - work. The
Bach, in _ ter_wo_ven With Spohr and Beet_ho_ven, At clas_sic _ al Mon_day Pops. The

la _ dy who dyes a che _ mi _ cal yel _ low, Or stains her grey hair puce, Or
bil _ liard sharp whom a _ ny _ one catches, His doom's ex _ treme _ ly hard— He's

pinches her fig _ ger, Is painted with vigour And per _ ma _ nent wal _ nut juice. The
made to dwell—In a dun _ geon cell On a spot that's al _ ways barr'd. And

i _ diot who, in rail _ way car _ ria _ ges, Scribbles on win _ dow _ panes, We
there he plays ex _ tra _ va _ gant matches In fit _ less fin _ ger _ stalls, On a

on _ ly suf _ fer To ride on a buf _ fer In Par _ lia _ men _ t'ry trains. My
cloth un _ true, With a twist _ ed cue, And el _ lip _ ti _ cal bil _ liard balls!

rall.   *a tempo*

rall.

object all sublime I shall achieve in time— To let the punishment

fit the crime-the punishment fit the crime; And make each pris_'ner pent Un_

_willingly re - pre_sent A source of in_nocent mer_ri_ment, Of innocent mer_ri_

CHORUS.

_ment! His ob_ject all sub_lime He will achieve in time— To

His ob_ject all sub_lime He will achieve in time— To

let the punishment fit the crime, The punishment fit the crime— And

let the punishment fit the crime, The punishment fit the crime— And

make each pris_'ner pent Un_wil_ling_ly re _ pre _ sent A

make each pris_'ner pent Un_wil_ling_ly re _ pre _ sent A

source of in_no_cent mer _ ri_ment, Of in_no_cent mer _ ri _ ment!

source of in_no_cent mer _ ri_ment, Of in_no_cent mer _ ri _ ment!

The

Nº 7. TRIO & CHORUS.—(Pitti-Sing, Ko-ko, Pooh-Bah, & CHORUS.)

1. The criminal cried, as he dropp'd him down, In a state of wild alarm— With a frightful, frantic, fearful frown, I bar'd my big right arm.—— I seiz'd him by his little pig-tail, And on his knees fell he, As he

squirm'd and struggled, And gur-gled and guggled, I drew my snick-er_snee,____ my snick-er_

_snee!____ Oh, never shall I For_get the cry, Or the shriek that shriek_ed

he,___ As I gnash'd my teeth, When from_ its sheath I drew_ my snick_er_

_snee!____ TUTTI & CHORUS.

We know him well, He can_not tell Un_true or groundless tales___ He

We know him well, He can_not tell Un_true or groundless tales___ He

al _ ways tries To ut _ ter lies, And ev _ 'ry time he fails.__

al _ ways tries To ut _ ter lies, And ev _ 'ry time he fails.__

PITTI-SING.

2. He shiv_er'd and shook as he gave the sign For the stroke he did_n't de _ serve; _ When

p

all of a sud_den his eye met mine, And it seem'd to brace his nerve; __ For he

nod_ded his head and kiss'd his hand, And he whis_tled an air,__ did he, As the

sa _ bre true Cut clean _ ly through His cer_vi_cal ver _ te _ brae, _____ his ver _ te_

_brae! _____ When a man's a_fraid, A beau_ti_ful maid Is a cheer_ing sight to

see; _____ And it's oh, _____ I'm glad That mo _ ment sad Was sooth'd by sight of

me! _____

CHORUS. *f*

Her ter_ri_ble tale You can't as_sail, With truth it quite a _ grees;_ Her

Her ter_ri_ble tale You can't as_sail, With truth it quite a _ grees;_ Her

taste ex-act For fault - less fact A - mounts to a dis - ease.

taste ex-act For fault - less fact A - mounts to a dis - ease.

POOH-BAH.

3. Now tho'you'd have said that head was dead (For its own - er dead was he), It

stood on its neck, with a smile well bred, And bow'd three times to me! It was

none of your im-pu-dent off - hand nods, But as hum - ble as could be; For it

clear _ ly knew The de_fer_ence due To a man of pe _ di _ gree, _____ of pe _ di _

_ gree! _____ And it's oh, I vow, This death _ ly bow Was a touch_ing sight to

see; _____ Though trunk_less, yet It could_n't for_get The de_fer_ence due to

me!

CHORUS.

This haugh_ty youth, He speaks the truth When_ev_er he finds it pays; _____ And

This haugh_ty youth, He speaks the truth When_ev_er he finds it pays; _____ And

Nº 8.   GLEE—(Pitti-Sing, Katisha, Ko-Ko, Pooh-Bah, and Mikado.)

DUET— Nanki-Poo and Ko-Ko,
(with Yum-Yum, Pitti-Sing, and Pooh-Bah.)

KO-KO.

The flowers that bloom in the spring, Tra la, Have no‐thing to do with the case. I've got to take un‐der my wing, Tra la, A most un‐attrac‐tive old thing, Tra la, With a ca‐ri‐ca‐ture of a face, With a ca‐ri‐ca‐ture of a face; And that's what I mean when I say, or I sing, "Oh, bo‐ther the flowers that bloom in the spring," Tra la la la la,— Tra

Tra la la la la,— Tra la la la la,—"Oh, bo-ther the flowers of spring!"

Tra la la la la, Tra la la la, Tra la la la la la!

Attacca

RECIT. & SONG— (Katisha.)

Andante moderato.

Hearts do not break! They sting and ache For old love's sake, But do not die! Though with each breath They long for death, As wit_nesseth The liv_ing I!— the liv_ing I!— Oh, liv _ ing I! Come, tell_ me_ why, When

hope is gone, Dost thou stay on?_____ Why lin_ger here, Where

all is drear? Oh, liv_ing I! Come, tell_ me_

why, When hope__ is gone, Dost thou_ stay on? May not a cheat_ed mai_den

die? May not_____ a cheated mai_den die?

SONG.—(Ko-Ko.)

ra_ther tough worm in your lit_tle in_side?" With a shake of his poor lit_tle

head. he re_plied, "Oh, wil_low, tit_wil_low, tit_wil_low!"

2. He slapp'd at his chest, as he sat on that bough, Singing

"Wil_low, tit_wil_low, tit_wil_low!" And a cold pers_pi_ra_tion be_

-span-gled his brow, Oh, wil-low, tit-wil-low, tit-wil-low! He—

sobb'd and he sigh'd, and a gur-gle he gave, Then he plunged himself in—to the

bil-low-y wave, And an e—cho a-rose from the su—i-cide's grave—"Oh,

wil-low, tit-wil-low, tit-wil-low!"   3. Now I

feel just as sure as I'm sure that my name Is_n't Wil_low, tit_wil_low, tit_

_wil_low,— That'twas blight_ed af_fec_tion that made him ex_claim, "Oh,

wil_low, tit_wil_low, tit_wil_low!" And if you re_main cal_lous and

ob_du_rate, I Shall per_ish as he did, and you will know why, Though I

pro_bab_ly shall not ex_claim as I die, "Oh, wil_low, tit_wil_low, tit_wil_low!"

DUET– (Katisha and Ko-Ko.)

that is so, Sing der-ry down der-ry! It's e-vi-dent, ve-ry, Our tastes are one. A-

-way we'll go, And mer-ri-ly mar-ry, Nor tar-di-ly tar-ry Till day is done!

KO-KO.

There is

beau-ty in ex-treme old age— Do you fan-cy you are el-der-ly e-nough? In-for-

_ma_tion I'm re_quest_ing On a sub_ject in_ter_est_ing: Is a mai_den all the bet_ter when she's

KATISHA.

tough? Through _ out this wide do_min_ion It's the gen_er_al o_pin_ion That she'll

KO-KO.

last a good deal long_er when she's tough. Are you old e_nough to mar_ry, do you

think? Won't you wait un_til you're eigh_ty in the shade? There's a

fas_ci_na_tion fran_tic In a ru_in that's ro_man_tic; Do you think you are suf_fi_cient_ly de_

-way we'll go, And mer-ri-ly mar-ry, Nor tar-di-ly tar-ry Till day is done! Sing

der-ry down der-ry! We'll mer-ri-ly mar-ry, Nor tar-di-ly tar-ry Till day is done.

FANFARE.

N.º 13. FINALE— ACT II.

Lowe and Brydone (Printers) Limited, London

END OF OPERA.

POPULAR COMIC OPERAS

By W. S. GILBERT and ARTHUR SULLIVAN

"THE GONDOLIERS" or "The King of Barataria"

"IOLANTHE" or "The Peer and the Peri"

"THE MIKADO" or "The Town of Titipu"

"PATIENCE" or "Bunthorne's Bride"

"THE PIRATES OF PENZANCE" or "The Slave of Duty"

"PRINCESS IDA" or "Castle Adamant"

"RUDDIGORE" or "The Witch's Curse"

"UTOPIA, LIMITED" or "The Flowers of Progress"

"TRIAL BY JURY"

"THE GRAND DUKE" or "The Statutory Duel"

"THE YEOMEN OF THE GUARD" or "The Merryman and his Maid"

*"H.M.S. PINAFORE" or "The Lass that Loved a Sailor"

*"THE SORCERER"

"HADDON HALL" by SYDNEY GRUNDY and ARTHUR SULLIVAN

"IVANHOE" by JULIAN STURGIS and ARTHUR SULLIVAN

VOCAL SCORES - PIANOFORTE SELECTIONS - LIBRETTI
EASY TO PLAY SELECTIONS - SEPARATE SONGS - VOCAL GEMS ALBUMS
PIANOFORTE SCORES - PART SONGS - CHORUSES

"THE FORESTERS," by LORD TENNYSON and ARTHUR SULLIVAN
The Songs, Choruses and Incidental Music, complete.
Selection for Piano.

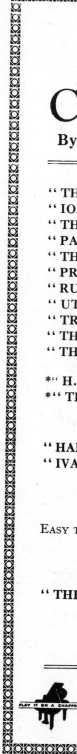

CHAPPELL & CO., LTD.,
50, NEW BOND STREET, LONDON, W.1
NEW YORK AND SYDNEY.

No. 3471